To SpongeBob's #1 Fan:

You are holding in your hands the first-EVER collection of SpongeBob comics. Pretty cool, huh? Some of these comics are more than ten years old, while some are brand-spanking-new. But all of these comics were created for *Nick Magazine*, mostly by the same artists who write and draw so many of the *SpongeBob* episodes you know and love.

That's where I come in. My name is Sherm Cohen, and I'm one of the *SpongeBob SquarePants* storyboard artists who worked on these comic stories. Now, some of you might be wondering, "What's a storyboard artist?" Well, a storyboard artist sketches the pictures for a *SpongeBob* cartoon, the first step in bringing a cartoon to life.

A comic is sort of like a storyboard before it gets animated for TV, except that a comic has word balloons, captions, sound effects, and tons of color! Storyboard artists can have loads of fun with comics because comics don't follow the same strict guidelines as TV. We can shake things up by using big panels and little panels. We can make a comic into a four-panel-long joke, or a ten-page adventure epic. And we can use all kinds of drawing styles—everything from the classic version of our favorite talking sponge to superfunky styles that make Bikini Bottom look crazy!

This collection combines comics of all shapes, sizes, lengths, and art styles . . . all brought to you by a bunch of cartoonists who love to tell funny stories.

These comics began life the same way a TV cartoon does: A handful of cartoonists sit around a table and toss ideas around until we find one that's full of funny possibilities and cool things to draw. For example, what would happen if SpongeBob got the hiccups and just couldn't stop? That little idea began to turn into an epic adventure when SpongeBob's creator, Stephen Hillenburg, suggested that Mr. Krabs might banish SpongeBob to a mythical place called Hiccup Island! My pal Derek Drymon suggested a journey to a spooky island haunted by the Flying Dutchman! I couldn't wait to get home and start sketching out the story while those images were flying around inside my head.

I had a great time drawing that story, and I'm really glad you'll have a chance to read that tale here, along with the rest of the best of the SpongeBob comic stories.

Enjoy!

Sherm Cohen
Storyboard Artist (one of many!)
and Storyboard Supervisor
For *SpongeBob SquarePants* (Seasons 1-4)

SpongeBob SquarePants™

Comic Crazy!

SIMON AND SCHUSTER/NICKELODEON

Stephen Hillenburg

Based on the TV series SpongeBob SquarePants created by Stephen Hillenburg as seen on Nickelodeon

SIMON AND SCHUSTER

First published in Great Britain in 2009 by Simon & Schuster UK Ltd
1st Floor, 222 Gray's Inn Road, London WC1X 8HB
A CBS Company

A CIP catalogue record for this book is available from the British Library

ISBN 978-1-84738-631-1

Printed in Singapore

3 5 7 9 10 8 6 4

"Prize Inside": Story, art, and lettering by Graham Annable. Colouring by Sno Cone Studios. "Hiccup! And Away!": Plot: Paul Tibbet. Script, art, and lettering: Sherm Cohen. Colouring: Digital Chameleon. Special thanks to: Stephen Hillenburg and Derek Drymon. "Just Desserts": Story, art, and lettering: C.H. Greenblatt. Colouring: Sno Cone Studios. "Krusty Krab Cleanup": Story: Paul Tibbit. Pencils: Mark O'Hare. Inks: Sherm Cohen. Colouring: Nick Jennings."Dollars and Scents": Story, art, and lettering: C.H. Greenblatt. Colouring: Sno Cone Studios. "Left Out": Plot: Sam Henderson. Script, pencils, and inks: Jay Lender. Colouring: Digital Chameleon. Lettering: Sherm Cohen. "Best Fiend": Story, art, and lettering: C.H. Greenblatt. Colouring: Digital Chameleon."Make that BigPants": Story: Walt Dohm, Art: Jay Lender, Lettering: Sherm Cohen, Colouring: Digital Chameleon."Gone Jellyfishing": Story: Derek Drymon and Sherm Cohen. Pencils: Scott Roberts. Inks and lettering: Vince Deporter. Colouring: Digital Chameleon."The Hole at the Bottom of the Sea": Story, art, and lettering: Sherm Cohen. Colouring: Digital Chameleon. "Dressed For Distress": Story, art, and lettering: C.H. Greenblatt. Colouring: Sno Cone Studios.

Special thanks to Stu Chaifetz. *Nick Magazine* SpongeBob comic staff: Andrew Brisman, Chris Duffy, Laura Galen, Tim Jones, Frank Pittarese, David Roman, Tina Strasberg, Catherine Tutrone, and Paul Tutrone. *Nick Magazine* would like to thank Stephen Hillenburg, Derek Drymon, and Sherm Cohen.

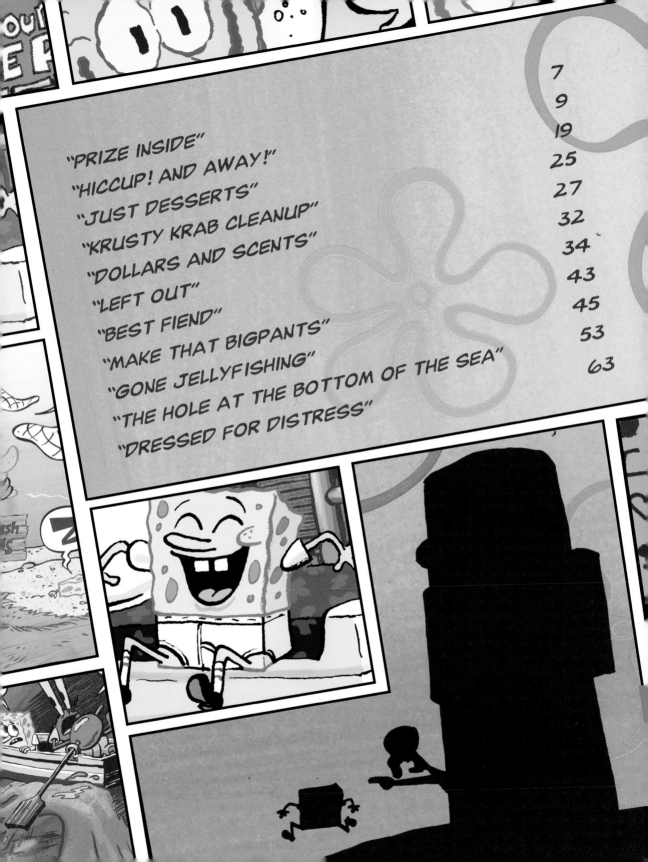

"PRIZE INSIDE" 7

"HICCUP! AND AWAY!" 9

"JUST DESSERTS" 19

"KRUSTY KRAB CLEANUP" 25

"DOLLARS AND SCENTS" 27

"LEFT OUT" 32

"BEST FIEND" 34

"MAKE THAT BIGPANTS" 43

"GONE JELLYFISHING" 45

"THE HOLE AT THE BOTTOM OF THE SEA" 53

"DRESSED FOR DISTRESS" 63

end!

13

The End

26

29

39

52

55

60

END